If I Were a Fish

Written by Susan Caver

Illustrated by Darcia Labrosse

MODERN CURRICULUM PRESS

MW00815203

Program Consultants

Becky Dugan, *Teacher*
Brady Elementary School
Little Rock, Arkansas

Judy Stobbe, *Bilingual Teacher*
Alianza School
Watsonville, California

Debra List, *Teacher*
Hansberry Child-Parent Center
Chicago, Illinois

Wanda Tansil, *Teacher*
University Terrace School
Baton Rouge, Louisiana

Executive Editor: Dorrie Berkowitz

Associate Editor: Marcia Formichelli

Design Concept: Lillie Caporlingua/BILL SMITH STUDIO

Copyright © 1995 by Pearson Education, Inc., publishing as Globe Fearon®, an imprint of Pearson Learning Group, 299 Jefferson Road, Parsippany, NJ 07054. All rights reserved. No part of this book may be reproduced or transmitted in any form or by any means, electronic or mechanical, including photocopying, recording, or by any information storage and retrieval system, without permission in writing from the publisher. For information regarding permission(s), write to Rights and Permissions Department. Published simultaneously in Canada by Pearson Education Canada.

ISBN 0-8136-8003-4 (single copy)   0-8136-8004-2 (6-pack)
Printed in the United States of America

2 3 4 5 6   09 08 07 06 05

Modern
Curriculum
Press

Pearson Learning Group

1-800-321-3106
www.pearsonlearning.com

If I were a fish in the sea, sea, sea,

a blue fish is what I would be, be, be.

Other colors are nice, too!

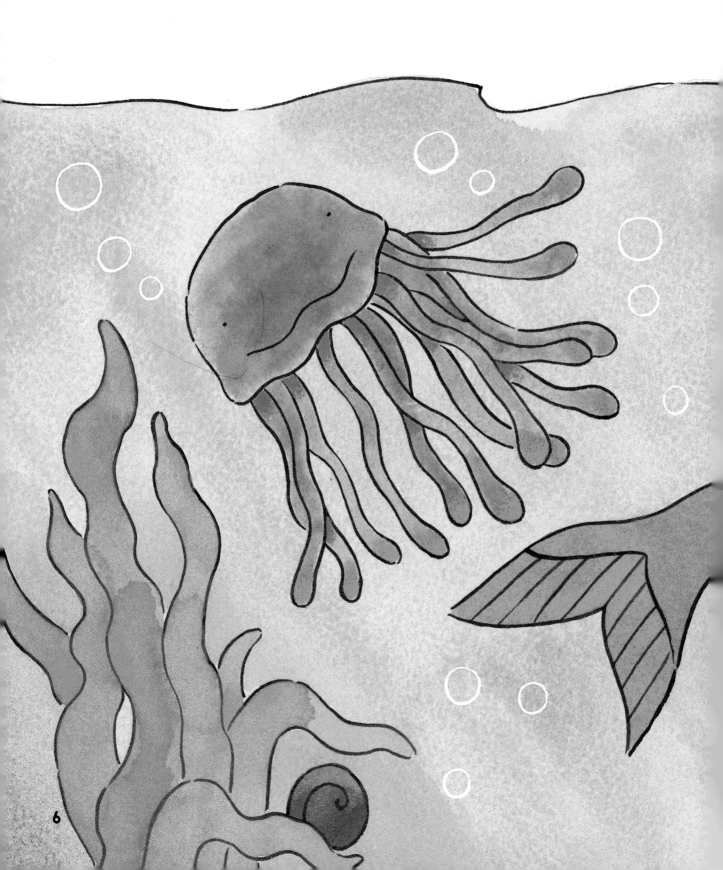

Do you know what I would do?

If I were a fish in the sea, sea, sea,

a red fish is what I would be, be, be.

Other colors are nice, too!

Do you know what I would do?

If I were a fish in the sea, sea, sea,

a yellow fish is what I would be, be, be.

Other colors are nice, too!

What do you think I should do?